Written by Sue Graves
Illustrated by Jan Smith (Advocate)
Designed by Blue Sunflower Creative

Language consultant: Betty Root

This is a Parragon book
This edition published in 2004

Parragon
Queen Street House
4 Queen Street
Bath, BA1 1HE, UK

ISBN 1-40542-204-1
Printed in China

Gold Stars

Big Digger
Helps Out

A Level 3 Reading Book

p

Notes for Parents

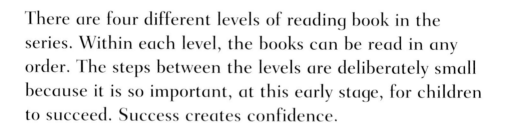

Reading with your child is an enjoyable and rewarding experience. These **Gold Stars** reading books encourage and support children who are learning to read.

There are four different levels of reading book in the series. Within each level, the books can be read in any order. The steps between the levels are deliberately small because it is so important, at this early stage, for children to succeed. Success creates confidence.

Starting to read

Start by reading the book aloud to your child, taking time to talk about the pictures. This will help your child to see that pictures often give clues about the story.

Over a period of time, try to read the same book several times so that your child becomes familiar with the story and the words and phrases. Gradually, your child will want to read the book aloud with you. It helps to run your finger under the words as you say them.

Occasionally, stop and encourage your child to continue reading aloud without you. Join in again when your child needs help. This is the next step towards helping your child become an independent reader.

Finally, your child will be ready to read alone. Listen carefully to your child and give plenty of praise. Remember to make reading an enjoyable experience.

Using your Gold Stars stickers

You can use the **Gold Stars** stickers at the back of the book as a reward for effort as well as achievement. Learning to read is an exciting challenge for every child.

Remember these four important stages:

- Read the story **to** your child.
- Read the story **with** your child.
- Encourage your child to read **to you**.
- Listen to your child read **alone**.

Big Digger is very big. Big Digger has a big bucket. The bucket can dig holes and move bricks.

Bert drives Big Digger. Bert and Big Digger work together.

Sometimes Bert and Big Digger work in the town. They help to dig holes in the road. They help fill in holes too.

Bert and Big Digger like digging
holes. But it can be very noisy!

Sometimes Bert and Big Digger work on the building site. Big Digger has to move bricks on the building site.

Bert and Big Digger like working on the building site. But it can be very noisy!

One day, Bert and Big Digger got a phone call. The phone call was from Mr Smith.

"Hello, Bert," said Mr Smith.
"I have lots of old bricks to move
from the building site. Can you and
Big Digger help?"

Bert and Big Digger went to the building site. They met Mr Smith.

"I want you to put the old bricks over there," said Mr Smith.

"Leave it to us, Mr Smith,"
said Bert.

Bert and Big Digger set to work.

Just then, Bert saw Little Bird.
Little Bird was sitting on her eggs.
The eggs were in a nest. The nest
was on top of an old drainpipe.

"Oh, no!" said Bert. "Look at that
nest, Big Digger. That is not
a safe place for eggs."

19

Bert put lots of straw into Big
Digger's bucket.
Big Digger lifted up his bucket.

He lifted it up to the top of the old drainpipe. Big Digger lifted the nest and the eggs into his bucket.

Wibble, wobble!

Big Digger moved the eggs to a tree.

"We will make a safe nest in the tree," said Bert. Bert and Little Bird made a safe new nest.

Big Digger lifted up his bucket.
He lifted it up to the new nest.
Bert put the eggs in the new nest.

Tweet, tweet!

"Look at Little Bird, Big Digger!" said Bert. "Look at Little Bird in her new nest. Now the eggs will be safe."

Little Bird sat on her eggs in her new nest.

"Now we must wait for the eggs to hatch," said Bert.

A few days later, Bert and Big Digger heard a noise. The noise was coming from the nest in the tree.

Tweet, tweet!

"Look, Big Digger!" said Bert. "The eggs have hatched. Thank you for helping Little Bird, Big Digger.

Read each sentence. The pictures will help you.

Bert and  work together.

Bert saw Little 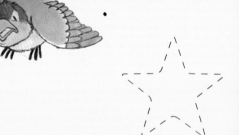.

Little Bird was sitting on her .

Big Digger took the
to the tree.

Bert made a nest in the .

put the eggs in the nest.

Gold Stars

Level 3 reading books are for beginner readers who can read short sentences with help.

- More detailed stories
- Builds essential vocabulary
- Speech bubbles repeat words from the main text
- Lively pictures to support the text
- Sentence review activity